This Box of Frogs book

For Theo and Mylo,

The Discombobulator

Written by Jane Clack
Illustrated by Lucy Spence

Jane Clack

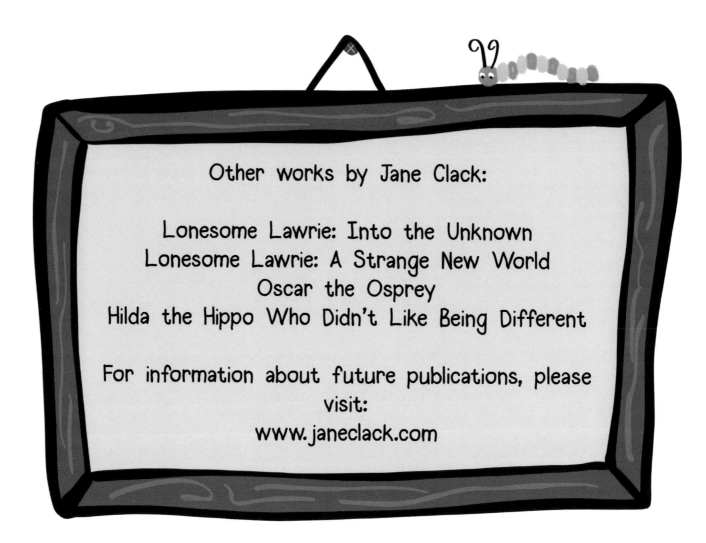

Other works by Jane Clack:

Lonesome Lawrie: Into the Unknown
Lonesome Lawrie: A Strange New World
Oscar the Osprey
Hilda the Hippo Who Didn't Like Being Different

For information about future publications, please visit:
www.janeclack.com

For Avery Mae.
Also with special thanks to Heather Gerry,
Ann Tharpe, Jill Watson and the children at
Alanbrooke Community Primary School

Foreword

In this book the Discombobulator is a unique, unusual and rather naughty creature that enjoys discombobulating all the animals around him by playing tricks on them.

Discombobulate

To upset, disconcert or confuse (someone or something).

Discombobulated

Addled, baffled, bamboozled, befogged, befuddled, bemused, bewildered, confounded, confused, disorientated, flummoxed, foxed, fuddled, muddled, mystified.

In a dark den, deep beneath the ground, the Discombobulator awoke. Rubbing the sleep away from his gritty eyes, he stretched and yawned.

"After a thousand-year-long nap,
I feel like being a naughty chap!" he chuckled to himself.

Crawling on all fours, he scrambled up the tunnel from his den until he began to see a bright light.

Quickening his pace, the Discombobulator soon reached the opening to the outside world.

He burst from the tunnel, stood up tall and stretched. He breathed in the sweet, clean air. It felt SO good!

Tall grass swayed in the field and an old oak tree towered high above him. He scratched his hairy back, and then his pointed horns, on the gnarled trunk of the tree. It felt GREAT!

Can you spot Kiki the Caterpillar?

She's hidden somewhere every time you turn the page.

The Discombobulator was pleased to see that he had company. A little way off stood a woolly lamb and a pudgy pink pig. The lamb was munching on the juicy grass and bleating contentedly. Her friend, the pig, was chomping happily on acorns and grunting with obvious pleasure.

The Discombobulator's eyes glinted mischievously.

"After so many years I'm feeling quite rusty,
So I'll begin with a spell that's tried and trusty.
There's no excuse for any delay;
It's a perfect pranking kind of day," he chortled to himself.

As the magic began to work, the lamb felt a quiver run down her fluffy, white tail and the pig felt a shiver run up his curly, pink tail. KAPOW!

"Oink ... boi.. baa," bleated the pig. His eyes opened wide and he stared at the lamb in disbelief:

"Your tail's become all curly and pink;
That seems distinctly odd I think!
And why am I bleating like a lamb?
Is this all part of a cunning plan?"

"Baa ... ba .. b .. oink," grunted the lamb. It sounded rather like a loud boink! She blinked in surprise. Looking at the pig she replied in dismay:
"Your tail's become all fluffy and white,
Unless someone's playing tricks with my sight.
The fact that I'm grunting is rather weird;
I've been discombobulated, just as I feared!"

Sniggering, and feeling extremely pleased with himself, the Discombobulator scampered off in search of more mischief. He rubbed his paws together gleefully.

"It's so much fun to be a prankster;
I take pride in being a rural gangster!"

Giggling, he set off in search of yet more trouble. It didn't take him long!

As he paused beside a pond, a movement caught the Discombobulator's eye. He watched with interest as a tadpole wriggled its way out of a lump of frogspawn. At the same time, a crunching sound above his head distracted him. It was a caterpillar feasting hungrily on a leaf.

A tremendously wicked idea flashed into the Discombobulator's brain.

"A strange transformation you'll both undergo,
But one of you will be filled with woe.
Although you'll be completely confused,
It'll keep me feeling wholly amused!"

As the trick began to work, the tadpole twisted and turned and the caterpillar wriggled and squirmed. KAPOW!

"WOW!" gasped the tadpole. She had pretty wings and she could fly.

"Goodness gracious, look at me,
This isn't how it's supposed to be!"

"RIBBUT," replied the caterpillar. He had a sticky tongue and could hop.

"Goodness gracious, look at me,
This isn't how it's supposed to be!"

"Your sensational makeover is now complete.
I'll not change you back, however you entreat," snickered the pesky Discombobulator.

"Suits me!" laughed the butterpole and flew away leaving the caterfrog sitting sadly on a rock.

"Awww, shucks," smirked the Discombobulator. "Never mind, I'm sure a nice juicy fly will soon come by!"

By now the Discombobulator was fizzing with energy and was on the lookout for even more fun.

"This day is too short for fitting in my fun,
I'll need to get a move on to get it all done.
I'm itching to make my spells dramatic,
And turn these creatures into something fantastic!"

He scratched the tousled fur between his horns and thought for a nanosecond.

"Eureka! I've got it, I know what I'll do:
I'll head straight down to the neighbouring zoo.
I'm impatient to greet them and say how do you do?
The spells that I cast will be strong and true!"

Chuckling with anticipation, he set off in the direction of the zoo.

The Discombobulator soon reached a large enclosure where a huge, yellow lion was lazily sunning himself and extending his sharp claws. When he yawned, his teeth glinted in the sunlight. From where he was watching, the Discombobulator could see a tiny mouse hiding fearfully in the shadows.

"My aim is to trick and to befuddle,
I'm going to cause a right old muddle.
A game of cat and mouse methinks,
This'll be an extraordinary jinx!" murmured the Discombobulator.

As the prank began to work, the lion's mane twitched and the mouse's whiskers itched. KAPOW!

Suddenly, the mouse pounced from the dark shadows, flexing his muscles and switching his long tail.

"RAAR!" he roared bravely at the lion, baring his tiny, sharp teeth.

"Crikey, I feel so courageous and strong.
Though pleasantly weird, something's very wrong!"

"Eek!" squeaked the cowardly lion, leaping away.

"Why am I so frightened of a tiny mouse?
To him I must be the size of a house!"

The Discombobulator jumped up and down excitedly when he saw the effect that the magic was having. Giggling, he set off in search of yet more challenges. Once again, it didn't take him long.

18

19

In a second enclosure prowled an elegant, spotted cheetah. She gazed unblinkingly at the Discombobulator and silently swished the tip of her tail. He stared back insolently. On some nearby grass stood a tortoise chewing on a limp lettuce leaf. An impish idea sprang into the Discombobulator's brain and he grinned broadly. He pointed rudely at the cheetah.

20

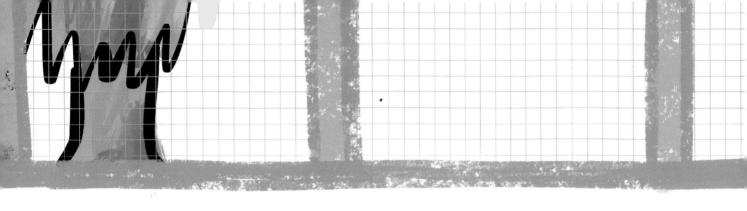

"You think you're so fleet, so fast, so cool,
But I'll make you look like an utter fool!
I'll give the tortoise your gift of speed,
And turn you into a slower breed."

As the hex began to work, the cheetah felt a shudder in her velvety paws while the tortoise felt a judder in his spindly claws.   KAPOW!

"WOW!   Now I'm as fast as a fancy racing car,
At these crazy speeds I'll travel far!" shouted the tortoise excitedly, and screeched off in a cloud of dust.   VROOM!   Within seconds, he was out of sight.

"The cheetah's withdrawn into her shell.
She's muddled by my awesome spell!" chortled the pesky Discombobulator.

The Discombobulator was utterly delighted with the chaos that he was causing: it was all just part of his dastardly plot.

"I wonder whose home is over there?" pondered the Discombobulator. "Perhaps I'll find an unfortunate pair."

Swaggering around the corner, the Discombobulator suddenly stopped short. He was captivated for a moment by what he saw. There before him stood the monkey house. On the grass in front of it strutted a beautiful, proud peacock displaying his impressive tail feathers. The Discombobulator felt as though a wonderful gift had just fallen right into his magical claws.

"Look at that monkey swinging there,
His bottom is so red and bare.
But the peacock's tail is beyond compare,
It makes me want to stand and stare!"

As the jinx began to work, the monkey felt a strange twerking sensation in his bottom and the peacock felt a strange jerking in his tail feathers. KAPOW!

"Ooh là là look at my derrière,
It gives me so much style and flair!" chattered the monkey proudly.

"My lady friends will swoon and sigh,
Gee whiz, I'm such a lucky guy!"

The peacock, embarrassed, sidled away.
It certainly wasn't his lucky day!

The Discombobulator guffawed loudly:

"It's great to cause such a hullabaloo;
I'll bet they're all pleased I came to their zoo."

23

A loud trumpeting sound diverted his attention to where a large elephant was flapping his ears and bellowing loudly;

"My memory's awesome, my knowledge rich;
My brain's as massive as a football pitch."

Despite all the noise, a skunk was snoring, undisturbed, beneath a nearby bush.

Pointing at the snoozing skunk, the rascally Discombobulator boldly addressed the elephant:

"I can't deny you're an impressive creature,
Your amazing memory's a remarkable feature.
But I'd like to cast a wondrous spell,
And gift you that skunk's interesting smell!"

As the enchantment began to work, the elephant felt a tremor in his trunk and the skunk was roused from her nap by peculiar vibes in her bushy tail.   KAPOW!

The elephant made a very rude sound, and a nasty smell wafted around.

THOSE WHO COULD RAN FOR COVER!!!

The skunk clamped her paws over her nose.

"If I smelled that bad, I'd decompose!" she groaned.

"But wait ...
My brain craves knowledge for facts and trivia.
I could memorise an encyclopaedia!"

The poor elephant replied sadly:

"My memory's foggy, dim and fuddled,
In fact I'm feeling completely muddled!
I've been afflicted with a terrible smell,
I feel really depressed and quite unwell."

24

25

The Discombobulator was now giddy with excitement. His desire to be naughty had reached fever pitch and he was eager to get up to even more tricks.

But little did he know that he was being watched from a tall tree by a wise old owl and his friend, the magpie.

"Oh goodness me, this will never do;
All these poor creatures are in a stew!" hooted the owl.

"That rascal never seems to learn ...
I think it's time he had a turn."

With that, the clever owl whispered something into the magpie's ear.

As quick as a flash, the magpie flew down from the branches of the tree and picked up a broken piece of mirror that was lying in the grass. He returned quickly to the owl's side. The owl hooted:

"Hey, Discombobulator. I've a message for you!"

Always be kind and honest and true,
And all these things will come back to you.

But if you're naughty and nasty, cruel and unkind,
All these things will revisit, you will find.

As we all learned long ago,
What you reap is what you sow.

Look into the mirror's bright reflection,
It'll point your magic in another direction."

Caught completely unaware, the Discombobulator glanced at the bright, shiny mirror that was dangling from the magpie's beak.

KAPOW!

ZAP!

BLAM!

KABOOM!

There was an enormous explosion of sound and colour.

"Your magic has bounced back to bewitch,
You're responsible for your own little glitch!

So back to your den is where you'll go,
To sleep for a thousand years or so.

Your broken state will reverse this calamity,
The other creatures will return to normality!

The Discombobulator quivered and shivered and twisted and turned. He twitched and itched and shuddered and juddered. He twerked and jerked and trembled and quaked.

Feeling feverish, the Discombobulator tried to howl, but all he could manage was a faint pig-like grunt. His tongue felt sticky, and stuck to the roof of his mouth. Glancing in the mirror, he was horrified to see that where he'd proudly sported horns, he now sprouted a little pair of flimsy wings. A shiny shell was clamped tightly to his back and his claws were webbed. To make matters even worse, the Discombobulator's tail had vanished in a puff of smoke and he'd been left with nothing but a big, bare, red bottom. The smell was terrible! He bleated:

"I've been tricked in the most deceitful way,
And for my bad behaviour I must pay.
By my own clever magic I'm all undone,
Just look at what I've now become!
I've been trumped by a stupid, silly old bird,
How utterly shameful and absurd.
My memory's foggy, dim and fuddled,
My magical spells forgotten and muddled.
I'm banished to sleep for a thousand years,
A very long time, so goodbye, my dears!"

With that, the Discombobulator sloped off back to his deep dark den.

"The moral of the story is so obvious but true:
Do only to others as you'd like done to you!
So before you're naughty, just think twice,
And always try to be pleasant and nice!

Twit twoo," hooted the wise old owl.

31

Fascinating Facts

In this section you'll be able to find out all kinds of interesting things about the creatures featured in this book! Please visit my website at janeclack.com, where you can download even more amazing facts about all the animals completely FREE together with a comprehensive glossary!

Are you up to the CHALLENGE? Go on, have a go!

Lifecycle of a Frog

- Frog eggs float in a jelly-like substance in a pond, these are called 'egg masses' or 'frogspawn'.

- Frogs lay thousands of eggs at a time! Many won't reach adulthood.

- Tadpoles hatch from the eggs and live in the pond.

- The tadpoles turn into froglets.

- The body shrinks and first the back legs and then the front legs grow.

- Next, the froglet's tail shrinks and its lungs develop.

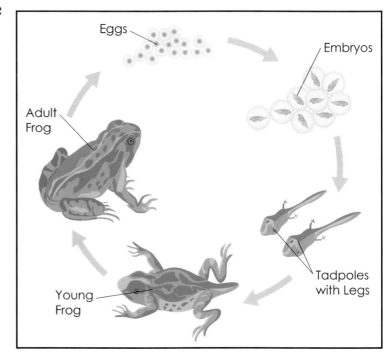

- The back legs grow more and then we have an adult frog.

Did you know?

- Frogs are amphibious. When they are developing, they breathe with gills.

- When they become adult frogs, they breathe with lungs.

- Amphibians shed their skin as they grow and the skin is usually eaten.
  The word 'amphibian' comes from the Latin word 'amphibium' and the Greek word 'amphibion' which means living both in water and on land.

- The lifecycle of a frog is a process called 'metamorphosis'.

Lifecycle of a Butterfly

- A butterfly starts life as a very small egg. The eggs are usually laid on leaves.

- When an egg hatches, the caterpillar (larva) will emerge.

- It immediately eats the leaf it was hatched on (most caterpillars are herbivores).

- They eat a lot so that they can grow quickly.

- As they grow they shed their exoskeleton several times.

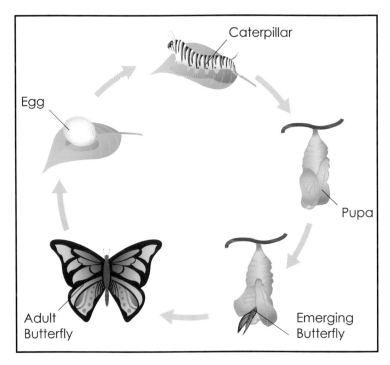

- Once the caterpillar has stopped growing it forms into a pupa (chrysalis/cocoon).

- While the caterpillar is inside the pupa, it is quickly changing and undergoing a metamorphosis.

- Finally, the butterfly emerges. When it first hatches its wings are soft, but after it has rested it pumps blood into its wings so that it can flap them. It can fly!

- The adult butterfly then reproduces and lays more eggs on a leaf.

- The life cycle is complete!

- This process is called 'metamorphosis'.

More bizarre animal facts!

- Sheep can recognise individual human faces and have good memories.

- A pig's genetic makeup is very similar to that of a human.

- If a lion breeds with a tiger, the resulting hybrids are called 'ligers' and 'tigons'.

- There are also lion and leopard hybrids known as 'leopons' and lion and jaguar hybrids known as 'jaglions'. How awesome is that?!

- Mice are one of the smallest mammals in the world.

- Cheetahs can purr.

- Tortoises can live to over 100 years old.

- Monkeys, just like humans, have their own unique set of fingerprints. A red bottom indicates that a female monkey is ready to reproduce.

- Peacocks (peafowl) are the national bird of India. In the Hindu religion peacocks represent compassion, benevolence, knowledge and kindness.

- Elephants truly have excellent memories. In fact, they have the largest brain of ANY animal!
Elephants can purr and they're also great swimmers.

- Skunks can hit a target with their smelly spray from 3.7 metres away. Some skunks spring into a handstand before spraying. They also stamp their paws, hiss and growl.

Owls can rotate their necks 270 degrees. They usually swallow their food whole and then regurgitate it as pellets. Owls are the symbol of learning.

According to myth, magpies like to collect and store shiny objects, but in fact they are actually scared of shiny objects and try to avoid them.

?

What do you think ligers, tigons, leopons and jaglions look like?

Don't forget to visit janeclack.com to find loads more information about all these unusual animals completely FREE!

The Challenge!

Answer the questions below and astound everyone around you with your incredible knowledge!

1.   Which animal has the largest brain?
2.   What is a female sheep called?
3.   Why do pigs roll in mud?
4.   What other name can you find for frogs' eggs?
5.   What does 'metamorphosis' mean?
6.   What name do you give to a creature that emerges from a butterfly egg?
7.   What is the collective noun for lion?
8.   What do you get if you cross a lion and a leopard (and no, this isn't a joke)?!
9.   What is a baby mouse called?
10.   What is the fastest land animal in the world?
11.   What are the scales on a tortoise's shell called?
12.   What group of animals do monkeys belong to?
13.   What is the smallest breed of monkey?
14.   What name do you give to a peacock's train?
15.   What is a male elephant called?
16.   What is a skunk's spray called?
17.   What is a male skunk called?
18.   How can you recognise a barn owl from the sound it makes?
19.   What is the collective noun for magpies?
20.   Who is famous for having used the word "Eureka!?"

Totally Terrible Jokes

Q. What do you call a thieving pig?
A. A hamburglar!

Q. What do you call a lamb that is covered in chocolate?
A. A candy baa!

Q. Why couldn't the frog tell the truth?
A. Because it was an am-FIB-ian!

Q. On which day do lions like to eat people?
A. On Chewsday!

Q. What does a tortoise do on his birthday?
A. He shellebrates!

Q. How many skunks do you need to make a terrible stink?
A. A phew!

Q. What is an owl's favourite subject?
A. Owlgebra!

Q. Why do monkeys like bananas?
A. Because they have appeal!

Q. What do you call a famous tortoise?
A. A shellebrity!

Q. What kind of cheese do mice like?
A. Mousearella!

Q. Who is the brainiest pig in the world?
A. Ein-swine!

Q. What does Kiki the caterpillar do on News Year's Day?
A. She turns over a new leaf!

Q. What kind of photographs do tortoises take?
A. Shellfies!

Q. Where does a peacock visit when he loses his tail?
A. A re-tail store!

Q. What do you call a monkey that is good at every sport?
A. A chimpion!